Twelve Pieces for Piano

In The Pink

Brian Chapple

Chester Music
(A division of Music Sales Limited)
8/9 Frith Street, London W1V 5TZ.

Performance Notes

'In The Pink' is the only piece that swings (♫ = ♩ ♪): there is no one correct speed, but I prefer it not to rush. 'Eleanor Ruth' is a happy, flowing piece: you can exaggerate the 'crescendo-that-leads-nowhere' (anticlimax) at the bottom of the first page.

'Copycat', 'Keeping Busy' and 'Mind The Gaps' benefit from a light touch, with plenty of contrast between legato and staccato in Nos. 4 and 9.

'Sticky Fingers' must be witty and, in spite of its title, crisp and neat using a firmer touch towards the end. 'Clever Clogs' is also witty, using a firm touch throughout, however, except in the last two bars.

'Far From Home' is perhaps the only really serious piece: use a singing tone and do not let the music drag. 'March Hare' looks more difficult than it is: do not forget that the quavers, whether staccato or legato, move at exactly the same speed in every bar.

Note that 'Swinging' moves fairly quickly (really one beat in a bar) and that the last two pieces (Nos. 11 and 12) are also fast. 'Danger, Keep Out!' must be rather stern and severe and 'Spanish Tummy' quiet fiery and very rhythmic.

B.C.

Brian Chapple

Brian Chapple lives just outside London, working as teacher and pianist as well as composer. He has written a wide variety of music: earlier pieces tended to be 'quirky' ('Scherzos' for four pianos, 'Trees Revisited' and 'Green And Pleasant'), whilst recent pieces are more serious ('Lamentations Of Jeremiah', 'Magnificat', 'In Memoriam', 'Requies', 'Missa Brevis').

The three volumes of piano pieces for beginners ('In The Pink', 'Lazy Days' and 'On The Cool Side') were written with his pupils in mind.

Brian Chapple enjoys gardening, drawing, France and all things French.

At present he is writing 'Crux', a choral work for Holy Week.

Exclusive Distributors:
Music Sales Limited
Newmarket Road, Bury St. Edmunds, Suffolk IP33 3YB.

ISBN 0-7119-3453-3
Order No. CH60885

Music processing by Ternary Graphics.
Printed in the United Kingdom by
Caligraving Limited, Thetford, Norfolk.

1. In The Pink

For My Great-Niece

2. Eleanor Ruth

Quite fast (♩. = c.64)

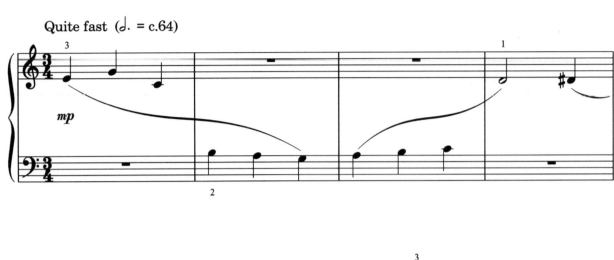

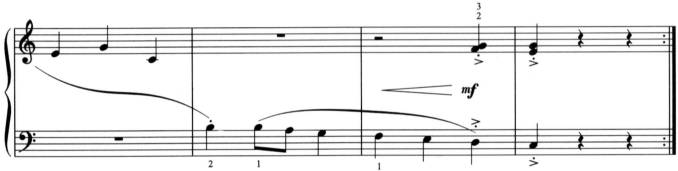

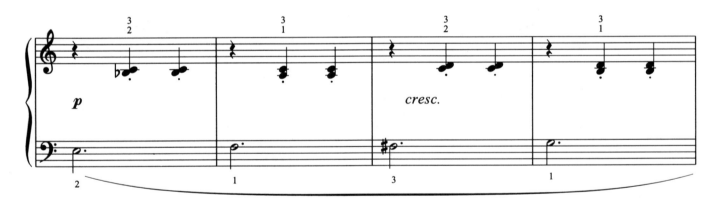

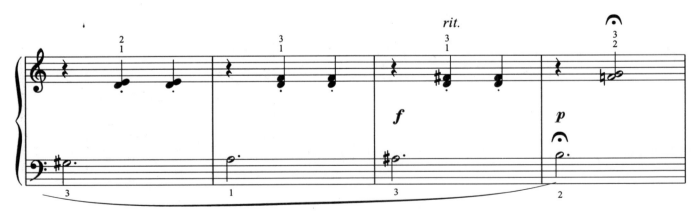

a tempo

3. Clever Clogs

Quite fast (♩ = c.144)

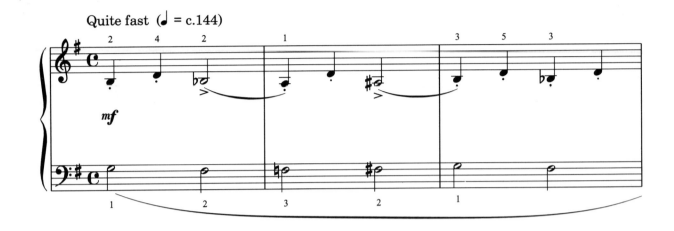

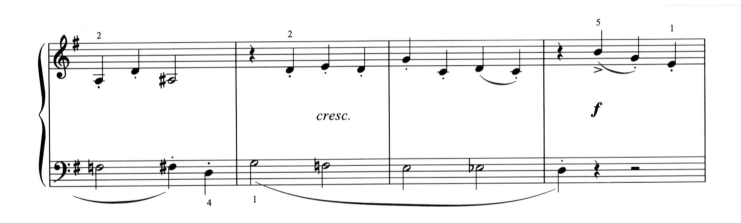

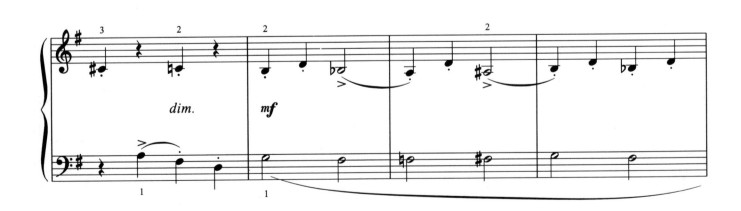

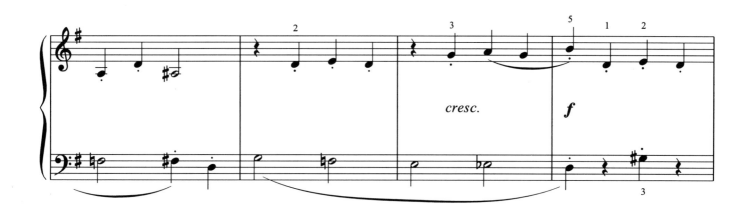

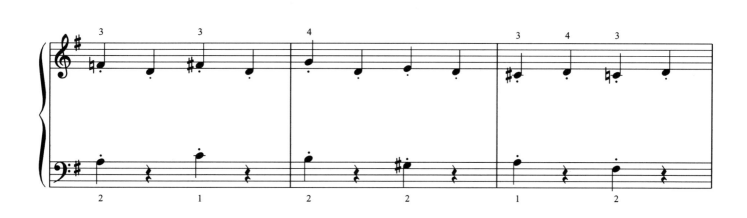

4. Copycat

With movement (♩ = c.120)

5. March Hare

6. Keeping Busy

Quite fast (♩ = c.90)

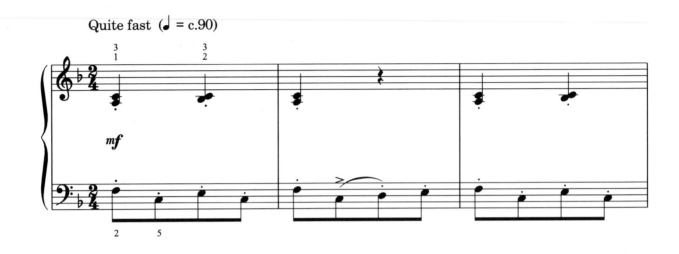

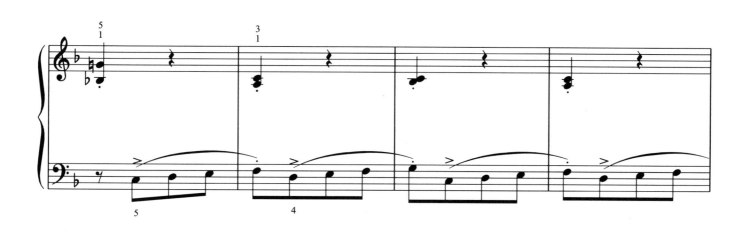

7. Far From Home

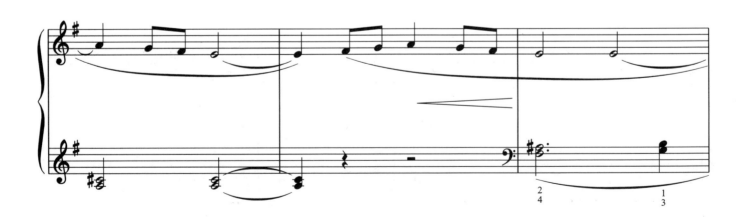

8. Sticky Fingers

Quite fast (♩ = c.144)

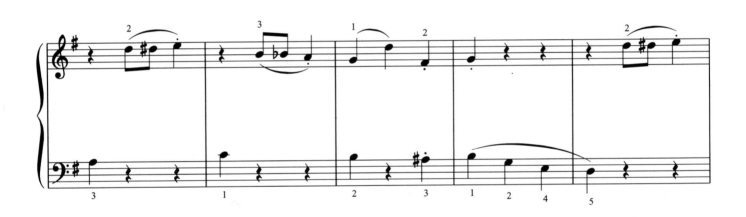

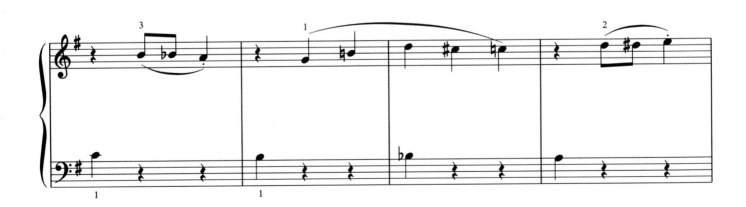

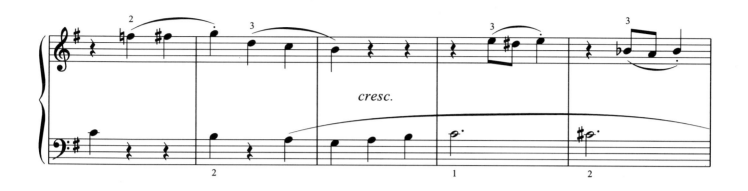

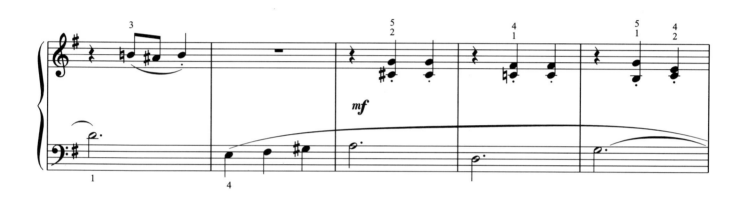

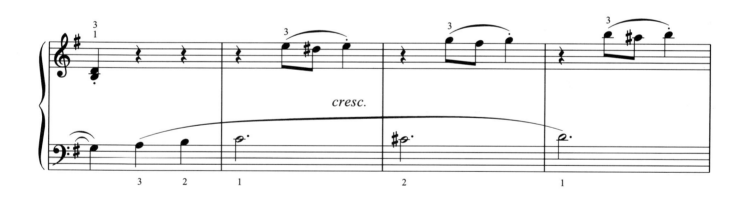

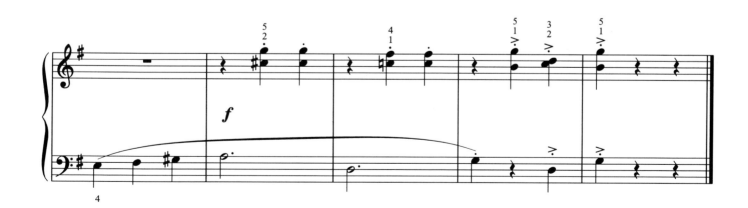

9. Mind The Gaps

Quite fast, but not rushed (♩ = c.78)

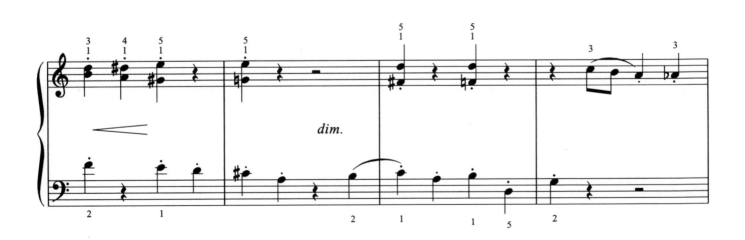

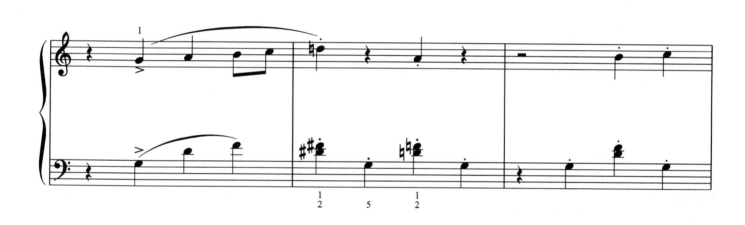
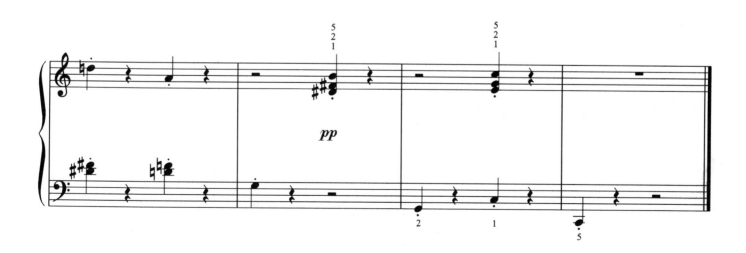

10. Swinging

Flowing (♩ = c.150)

11. Danger, Keep Out!

Quite fast, strict time (♩ = c.156)

12. Spanish Tummy

Fast (♩ = c.168)